The
# CAMERA PHONE
# ILLUSION BOOK
by
Jim Sharp

First published in Great Britain in 2016

ISBN 978-1-527-26674-2

Design by Jim Sharp and Roy Sharp
Printed and Bound in Great Britain by Printfine, Liverpool

# INTRODUCTION

'The camera never lies' is a common phrase but the illusions in this book will demonstrate that the opposite can be true.

Use your camera phone to view or photograph each page - the images that appear on your phone will surprise you.

Duillusions are two images in one.
When edge lines from contrast breaks of one image are added to the soft focus tones of a second image, a peculiar illusion occurs. Look closely and you see the first image but as you move away (or view with your camera phone) the edge lines become thin and lose their influence allowing the second image to dominate the view.
If you do not have a camera phone you can view them from about two metres away (6 feet) to see the effect.

Stretched Anamorphic images can be seen by viewing with your camera phone from an acute angle. These are difficult to see normally but when the camera phone lens is placed at an angle close to the edge of the page, hidden images and messages are revealed.
This technique was used by artists hundreds of years ago.

3D Anamorphic illusions make the images look 3D when viewed from a certain position similar to the floor graphics that are popular today. These illusions can be viewed with your camera phone and will look like you have just taken a photograph of a real 3D model that was actually there! Use flash for the best effect.

I hope you enjoy these illusions and share the experience with your friends.

Jim Sharp, August 2016

Here is the first Duillusion for you.
Look at it through your camera phone to see
the secret message hidden behind the letters.

# BLACK
## TURNS INTO
# WHITE

# THE
# CAMERA
# NEVER
# LIES

Which way is Frankenstein's monster looking? Take a picture with your camera phone and he will appear to be looking the opposite way.

Your camera phone can perform a clever magic trick for you...
Take a picture from about 30cm away but don't zoom in and the Queen of Diamonds will turn into the Jack of Clubs!

All that glitters is not GOLD.
Take a picture from 30cm away to see why!

Here are some names of capital cities.
Take a picture with your camera phone to
reveal the countries they are in.

PYONGYANG
ANKARA
BANGKOK
ACCRA
LIMA
BUCHAREST
KAMPALA
Greenland (Dk.)
Greenland Sea
Svalbard (Nor.)
Barents Sea
Norwegian Sea
Iceland
Sweden
ATLANTIC
OCEAN
Angola
Zambia
Malawi
Comoros
Madagascar
Namibia
Zimbabwe
Mozambique
Botswana
Swaziland
Lesotho
South Africa
Mauritius
Oman
Cape of Good Hope
St. Helena
Tristan da Cunha

Which is the largest city in China?
Its name is hidden but you can reveal it by
taking a picture with your camera phone!

隐藏的信仰、信念、文化

隐藏的信仰、信念、文化

Look closely.
Is this a picture of Marilyn Monroe or is it the
famous painting of the Mona Lisa?
Look at the image on your camera phone
before you decide.

This famous poster has a hidden message. Take a picture with your camera phone to reveal what it really says!

'Dial-a-Dali' could be the perfect title for this Duillusion.
Look with your camera phone and you will see an image of the artist.

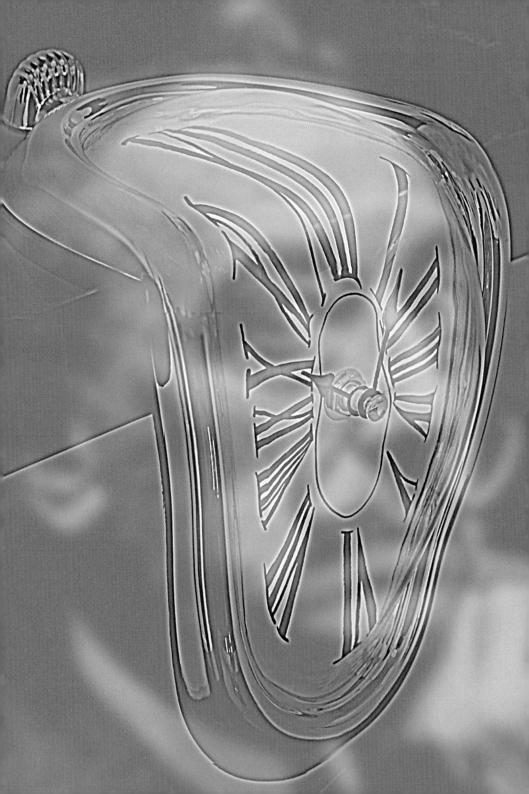

Write down a three digit number.
Then write that number in reverse.
Subtract the smaller number from the bigger
number.

Take that answer and reverse it, then add those
two numbers together.

Take a picture of the page opposite and it
should reveal the same number.

Example: 743
Reverse it: 347 (smaller number)
743 - 347 = 396
Reverse it: 693
693 + 396 = ?

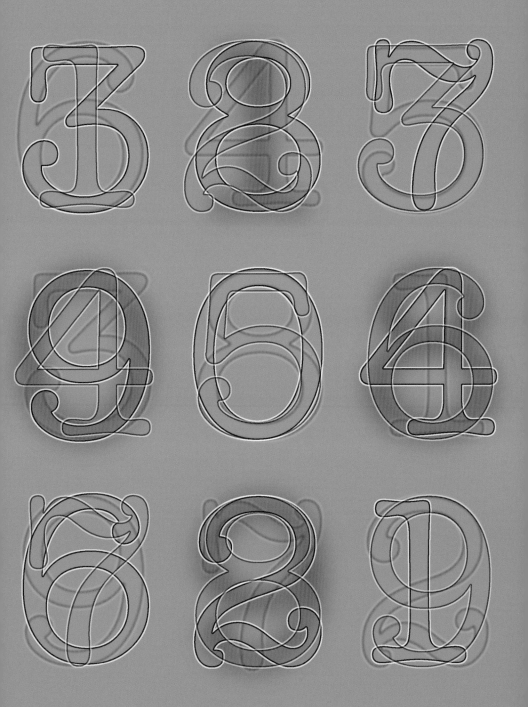

View this early Victorian 'Penny Black' postage stamp on your camera phone and the image of Queen Victoria will magically change into Queen Elizabeth II as seen on our modern day first class stamps.

# Great Britain

Great Britain issued the world's first postage stamp (the 'Penny Black' of 1840). Her stamps do not bear the name of the country, the head of the sovereign being considered

also commemorated. Capital: London. Currency: 100 pence = 1 pound.

We hope the makers of Marmite don't mind us using their product for this Duillusion.
They will either love it or hate it!
View the image on your camera phone to see what the camera thinks of it.

Take a photo with your camera phone to translate this Klingon message into English.

Take a picture of this One Pound Coin from about 30cm (12") away and your camera will change it into One Penny.

From a distance this road safety sign reads 'SLOW DOWN' then it changes to 'THANK YOU' as you approach it.
Take a picture with your camera phone from about 30cm away and you will see it change.

View this picture of Albert Einstein on your camera phone and you will see how he looked as a young boy.
Your camera is now a time machine!

Here is an unusual shop door sign.
From across the street it says OPEN but when
you get to the door they are CLOSED!
Take a picture with your camera phone and
you too will be confused!

## Instructions for viewing.

3D Anamorphic distortions look like they are actually standing up from the page when you view them on your camera phone.

Open the book to 90° and take a picture from a point diagonally opposite from the far corner and from about the same height as the top of the book.

Use flash for best results.

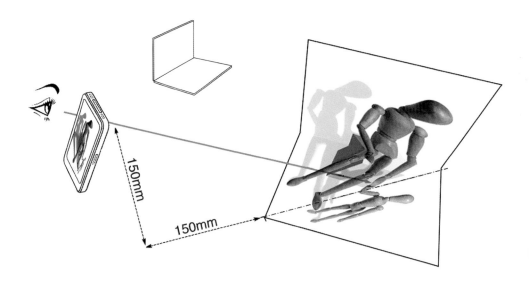

150mm

150mm

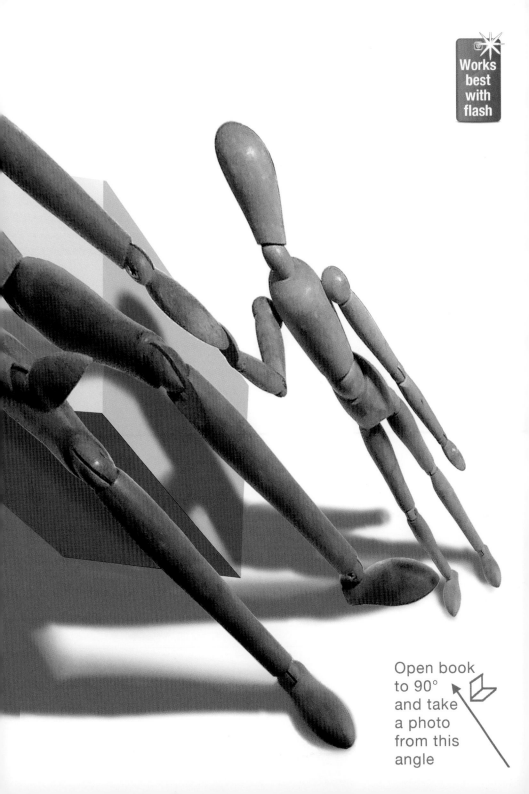

Open book
to 90°
and take
a photo
from this
angle

Works
best
with
flash

Open book
to 90°
and take
a photo
from this
angle

Open book to 90° and
take a photo from this angle

Works best with flash

Open book to 90° and take a photo from this angle

Works best with flash

Open book to 90°
and take a photo
from this angle
with the camera lens
at the same height
as the left hand page

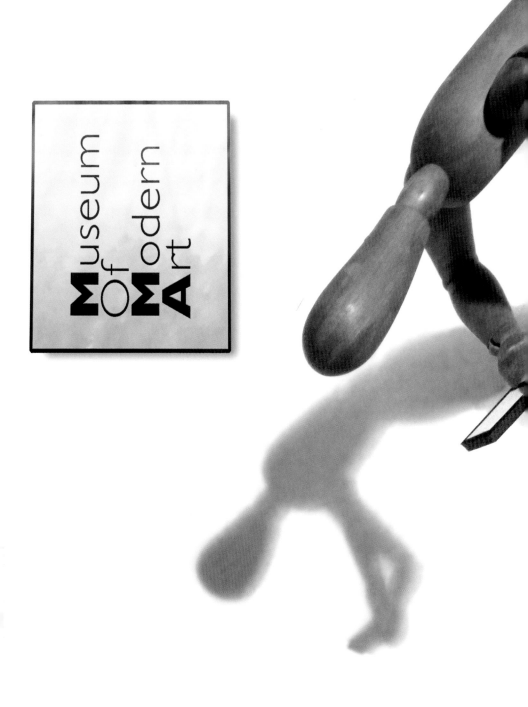

Works best with flash

Open book to 90° and take a photo from this angle

3D • GLASSES

Open book
to 90°
and take
a photo
from this
angle

Works best with flash

Open book to 90° and take a photo from this angle

Works
best
with
flash

Open book
to 90°
and take
a photo
from this
angle

Open book
to 90°
and take
a photo
from this
angle

Anamorphic distortions are stretched images.

In Victorian times it was used as a way of sending secret messages on novelty postcards.

Take a picture from the edge of the page at a low angle and all will be revealed.

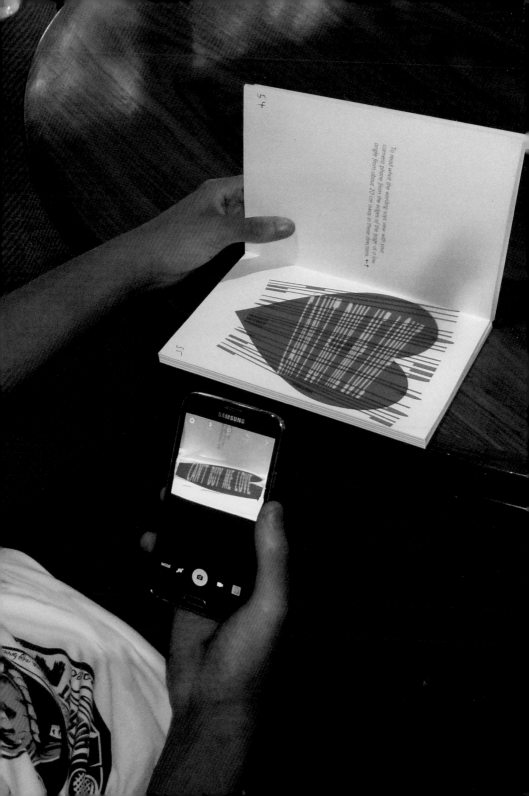

To read what the wording says view with your camera phone from the edges of the page at a low angle from about 20 cm away in these directions →↑↓

**The Ambassadors**
by Hans Holbein the Younger, 1533

An early example of anamorphic art is the distorted skull painted by Hans Holbein across his painting titled 'The Ambassadors' which he created in 1533.

Take a picture from the direction of the red arrow at a low angle and you will see the skull in its correct proportions.

To read what the wording says, view with your camera phone from the edges of the page at a low angle from about 20 cm away in these directions: ←↑

These pulses from space can be decoded by taking a picture from the edge of the page in this direction: ←

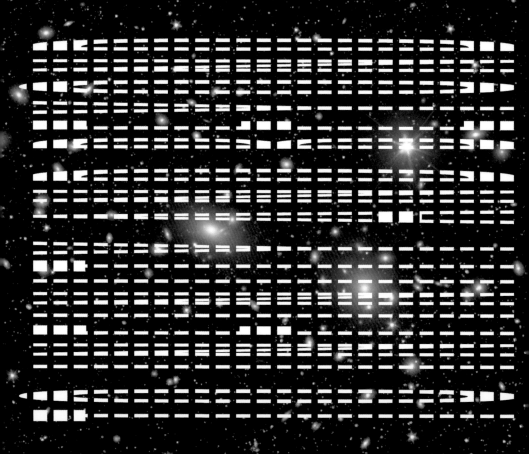

Dwarf Galaxies + Spiral Galaxy M81

Photograph from the direction of the arrows at a low angle from about 20 cm away to reveal some healthy advice.

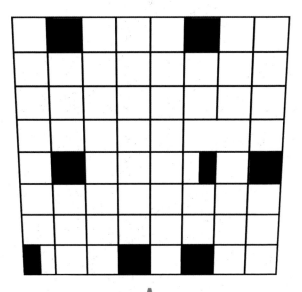

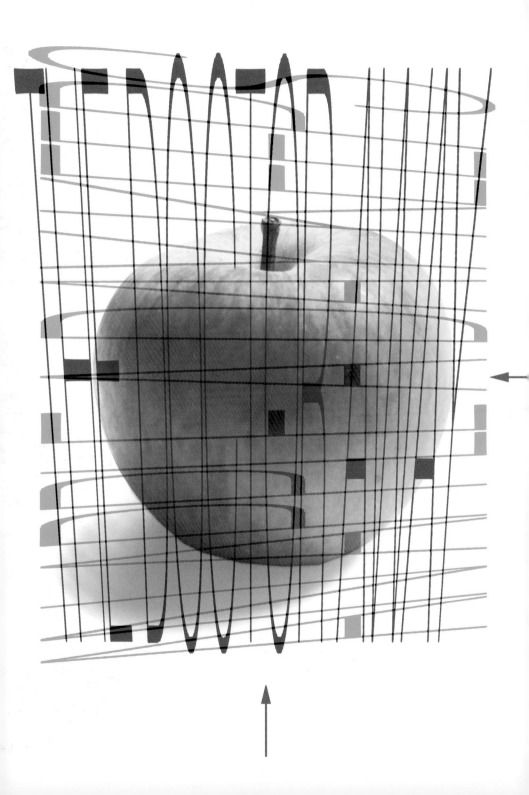

Place your camera phone in the centre of the record, as in the illustration below, then rotate it to reveal some Beatles titles from their 'Meet The Beatles!' LP.

Meet The
BEATLES!

1

Place your camera phone
lens in the middle of the
record and rotate to
reveal some
Beatles Titles

The Rosetta Stone found in 1799 had three versions of the same text in different languages, enabling scholars to decypher ancient texts.

The stone opposite has a hidden message that can be revealed by viewing it from the edge of the page with your camera phone at a low angle.

...tique ligula feugiat nec. Nam a ris...
...tellus nec dictum tincidunt, ante odio gravi...
...quis ullamcorper nisl ullamcorper sed. Sed liber...
...commodo eu elementum non, tempus laoreet velit. Praes...
...trices enim, in faucibus velit lectus vitae metus. Vestibulum...
...pit. Maecenas ut justo ligula. Vestibulum eleifend vulputate erat, l...
...nunc facilisis et ultrices massa pharetra. Etiam at nunc odio, nec accum...
...us scelerisque vitae congue sem. Phasellus porta nisl in enim congue pellent...
...a. Aenean mi augue, elementum a dignissim eu, tristique ut odio. Sed a blandit f...
...el, laoreet vitae neque. Praesent vehicula tellus ac mi imperdiet cursus. Nulla acc...
...erdum dignissim nisi, quis tristique ligula feugiat nec. Nam a risus elit. Mauris soll...
...is a.Suspendisse malesuada, tellus nec dictum tincidunt, ante odio gravida augue, a su...
...feugiat lobortis massa, quis ullamcorper nisl ullamcorper sed. Sed libero dui, ultrices si...
...que. Proin diam arcu, commodo eu elementum non, tempus laoreet velit. Praesent commodo, neque...
...ortor lacus ultrices enim, in faucibus velit lectus vitae metus. Vestibulum ac urna nulla. Aliquam...
...m suscipit. Maecenas ut justo ligula. Vestibulum eleifend vulputate erat, hendrerit semper libero...
...t id nunc facilisis et ultrices massa pharetra. Etiam at nunc odio, nec accumsan tellus. Nam vitae felis...
...erdum rieus, eu simod sagittis ligula tincidunt dictum. Nulla facit. Sed vestibulum lacinia erat vitae...
...ti sociosqu ad litora torquent per conubia nostra, per inceptos himenaeos. Proin rhoncus consequat ele...
...est et tellus interdum sagittis.Donec sit amet dui at nulla aliquet mattis. Vestibulum facilisis aliquet mi n...
...faucibus tincidunt velit porttitor sodales enim interdum et. Vivamus ligula metus, eleifend sed condimentum sed,...
...non mauris id elit tempus dictum ac ac erat. Fusce fringilla eros sed est egestas in cursus erat imperdi...
...erisque adipiscing. Maecenas egestas est non metus egestas gravida. Vestibulum ante ipsum primis in faucibus o...
...posuere cubilia Curae. Fusce sit amet ultricies tellus. Phasellus at odio magna, ut suscipit purus. Nulla facil...
...rem eget lorem molestie, turpis mauris molestie erat, sed placerat lorem magna eget augue. Donec non velit u...
...t, faucibus a elementum vel, commodo ut sem. Integer risus erat, adipiscing nec molestie eu, ullamcorper non a...
...elit purus. Pellentesque dictum, dolor eget dignissim porta, velit orci sollicitudin purus, ut cursus risus felis...
...cus, blandit vel sagittis ut molestie et metus. Lorem ipsum dolor sit amet consectetur adipiscing elit. Quisqu...
...andrit porttitor. Nam eros risus, posuere in elementum sed, dictum in arcu. Aliquam quis erat non metus bibendu...
...du. Sed tincidunt nulla quis neque pretium non sollicitudin massa interdum. Aenean pellentesque rutrum nunc...
...raesent eros nisl sit amet erat facilisis vehicula Vitae vel mi. Aliquam sed augue in magna blandit, bene...
...uris sit amet eros gravida aliquam id ac est. Morbi eget sem eget massa ultricies fringilla ac in ante. Pellentesqu...
...lamcorper blandit elit quam sodales velit, vel vestibulum quam id velit vitae arcu. Nam tristique ante eu est egestas...
...lor, sollicitudin non consequat et, vulputate vitae ante. Sed at metus eu dolor aliquet molestie non tincidunt...
...n, tristique eges suspendum ut venenatis sit amet nibh. Nunc eget ligula non magna porttitor posuere adipiscing...
...onsectetur elit ut dolor posuere feugiat. Aliquam eu vulputate velit. Nullam ut nibh in quam imperdiet adipiscing...
...egerda vel aliquat ut, ultricies in arcu. Cras cursus justo vestibulum risus consectetur eget porta sapien fermentu...
...que. Lorem ipsum dolor sit amet, consectetur adipiscing elit. Duis a sem elit, vel ultricies est. Donec faucibus d...
...cidunt. Morbi vitae elit non lorem cursus scelerisque vitae congue sem. Phasellus porta nisl in enim congue peller...
...aretra nulla sem, at venenatis ligula. Aenean mi augue, elementum a dignissim eu, tristique ut odio. Sed a blandi...
...tellus, dignissim ac consectetur vel, laoreet vitae neque. Praesent vehicula tellus ac mi imperdiet cursus. Nulla a...
...odio et tristique. Maecenas interdum dignissim nisi, quis tristique ligula feugiat nec. Nam a risus elit. Mauris solli...
...im, nec suscipit sem mattis a.Suspendisse malesuada, tellus nec dictum tincidunt, ante odio gravida augue, a suscipi...
...turpis. Suspendisse feugiat lobortis massa, quis ullamcorper nisl ullamcorper sed. Sed libero dui, ultrices si...
...eu, lobortis quis purus. Proin diam arcu, commodo eu elementum non, tempus laoreet velit. Praesent commodo, nec...
...uris sit amet eros gravida aliquam id ac est. Morbi eget sem eget massa ultricies fringilla ac in ante. Pellentesque a...
...ullamcorper blandit, elit quam sodales velit, vel vestibulum quam velit vitae arcu.Nam tristique ante eu est egestas lu...
...dolor, sollicitudin non consequat et, vulputate vitae ante. Sed at metus eu dolor aliquet molestie non tincidunt augu...
...en eget bibendum ut, venenatis sit amet nibh. Nunc eget ligula non magna porttitor posuere ad piscing et...
...onsectetur elit ut dolor posuere feugiat. Aliquam eu vulputate velit. Nullam ut nibh in quam imperdiet adipiscing. In...
...lesuada vel aliquatut, ultricies in arcu. Cras cursus justo vestibulum risus consectetur eget porta sapien fermentum...
...eque. Lorem ipsum dolor sit amet, consectetur adipiscing elit. Duis a sem elit, vel ultricies est. Donec faucibus...
...ncidunt. Morbi vitae elit non lorem cursus scelerisque vitae congue sem. Phasellus porta nisl in enim congue sem...
...haretra nulla sem, at venenatis ligula. Aenean mi augue, elementum a dignissim eu, tristique ut odio. Sed a bl...
...s tellus, dignissim ac consectetur vel, laoreet vitae neque. Praesent vehicula tellus ac mi imperdiet cursus...
...odio et tristique. Maecenas interdum dignissim nisi, quis tristique ligula feugiat nec. Nam a risus elit...
...nim, nec suscipit sem mattis a.Suspendisse malesuada, tellus nec dictum tincidunt, ante odio gravida augue...
...turpis. Suspendisse feugiat lobortis massa, quis ullamcorper nisl ullamcorper sed. Sed libero du...
...eu, lobortis quis purus. Proin diam arcu, commodo eu elementum non, tempus laoreet velit. Praes...
...vada scelerisque, tortor lacus ultrices enim, in faucibus velit lectus vitae metus...

This 'Pixel' effect is used in media to disguise faces. Take a picture on your camera phone from about 40cm away and don't zoom in - you should be able to recognise who it is.

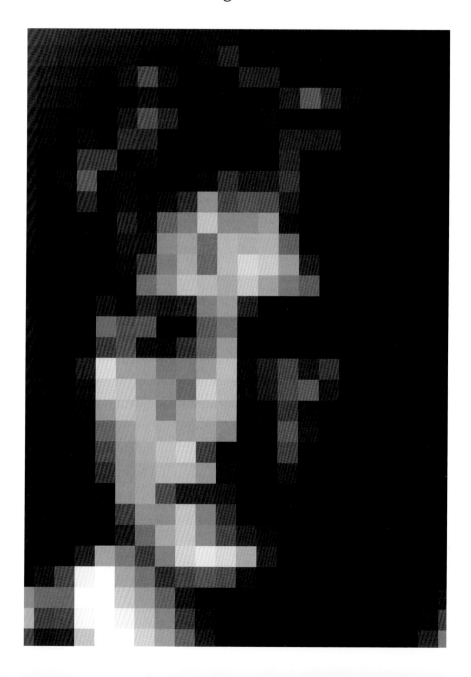

Litho printing uses cyan, magenta, yellow and black ink to print a colour picture in tiny halftone dots. This enlarged colour halftone of a famous artist will look clearer in your camera viewer.

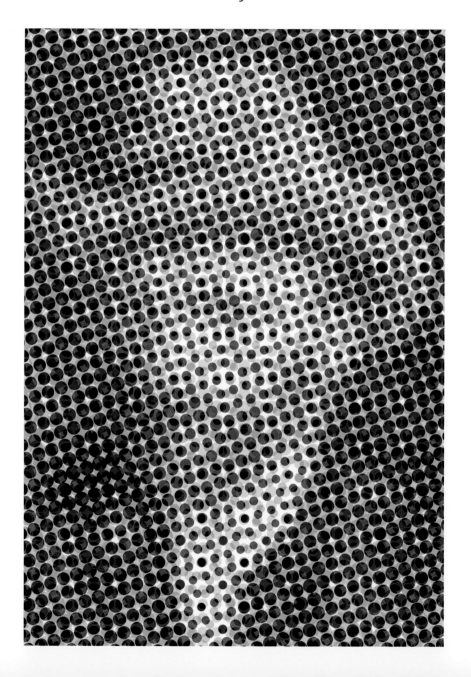

# INTERESTING EYE FACTS

On average, we blink 12 times per minute - which is about 11,500 blinks per day and more than four million times per year.

The human eye can see about 10 million colour hues.

The human eye can distinguish 500 shades of grey.

All babies are colour-blind when born.

In the right conditions, the human eye can see the light of a candle from 14 miles away.

Your eyes are able to process 36,000 items of information each hour.

Your eyes contribute to about 85% of your total knowledge.

Eyes began to develop 550 million years ago. The simplest eyes were patches of photoreceptor protein in single-celled animals.

Your eyeballs stay the same size from birth to death, while your nose and ears continue to grow.

An eye is composed of more than 2 million working parts.

80% of our memories are determined by what we see.

A fingerprint has 40 unique characteristics, but an iris has 256, a reason retina scans are increasingly being used for security purposes.

You see with your brain, not your eyes. Our eyes function like a camera, capturing light and sending data back to the brain.

Dogs can't distinguish between red and green.

20/20 vision simply means that you have normal vision.

People generally read 25 times slower on screen than on paper.

An ostrich's eye is bigger than its brain.

The human eye only sees three colours; red, blue and green. All other colours are a combination of these.

Your eyes contain 7 million cones which help you see colour and detail, as well as 100 million cells called rods which help you to see better in the dark.

Oily fish, vitamin A and vitamin C all help to preserve good eyesight.

You see things upside down - it is your brain which turns the image the right way up.

Peripheral vision is very low-resolution and almost in black and white.

Your eye is constantly making tiny jerking movements called 'microsaccades' to stop objectives fading from vision.

Synesthesia is the name of the condition of seeing colours when sounds are heard. Some musicians can see colours when listening to music.

Prosopagnosia is what you have if you cannot recognise faces. In serious cases, faces of close family or friends are not recognised.

Eyes are the second most complex organ after the brain.

## About the author.

Jim Sharp was born in Liverpool in 1942. He attended the Liverpool School of Art and then worked as an artist in an advertising agency.

At the age of 21 years in 1963 he started McCaffrey and Sharp Commercial Art Studio with his business partner Stan McCaffrey.

In 1975 he invented and patented the Schafline High Definition System which became very successful and was franchised world-wide. It increased the definition of newspaper images by adding black and white 'Schafline' edge lines to the screened halftone image.

Then in 1982 he started Pinsharp 3D Graphics to serve the demands of the new 3D graphics market and produced 3D conversions for many well known brands, advertising agencies and publishers.

Recently he produced a short nine-minute video entitled 'The Blinking Third Eyelid' which is about how birds might see their world.

His new Duillusion® effect is a result of his many years of experience in visual perception.

Thanks to the following for their help in bringing this book to life:

Rita Sharp, Roy Sharp, Janet Sharp, Andrew Small,
David Burder, Alf Menzies, Brian Higgins, National Gallery,
Wikipedia, Shutterstock, The Illustrated London News Archive,
and all who have given their time testing the illusions.